EQUIZ
Novice

British Library Cataloguing in Publication Data
A catalogue record for this book is available from the British Library

ISBN 0.85131.653.0

Published in Great Britain in 1996 by
J. A. Allen and Company Limited,
1 Lower Grosvenor Place,
Buckingham Palace Road,
London, SW1W OEL.

Typeset in Great Britain by Textype Typesetters, Cambridge.
Printed in Great Britain by Hillman Printers (Frome) Ltd, Somerset.

EQUIZ
Novice

VANESSA BRITTON

J. A. Allen
London

PART 1

Horse management

Anatomy and physical characteristics

1 Which is the odd one out?

a) Bay. ☐

b) Hack. ☐

c) Chestnut. ☐

2 What head marking is being discussed?

This white marking covers part of the muzzle and extends up over the nose and eyes, including the forehead.

3 Join up the sentences.

a) A stocking **i)** is a white mark between the nostrils.

b) A sock **ii)** extends no further than the fetlock.

c) A snip **iii)** extends as far as the knee or hock.

4 On the diagram (page 6), mark the following physical characteristics:

a star and a snip
a white sock on the left fore
a stocking on the right fore
a white coronet on the left hind
a freeze mark on the left side bearing the brand A100

identical whorls on each side of the neck line, midway from ears to withers.

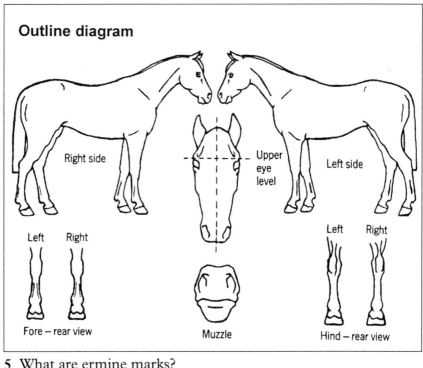

Outline diagram

5 What are ermine marks?

a) They are white marks on a black leg. ☐
b) They are black marks on a white leg. ☐
c) They are white flecks throughout the body. ☐

6 What is the term used to refer to the measurement taken right round the foreleg just below the knee?

_____

_____

7 True or false?

a) A foal is a young horse up to the 1st of January following its birth.   true ☐   false ☐

b) A weanling is a young horse between the ages of two and three.   true ☐   false ☐

c) A colt is a young male horse up to the age of three years. true ☐   false ☐

8 From the list below, fill in the labels to name the parts of the horse.

muzzle   **stifle**
forearm   **loins**
ergot   **windpipe**
point of buttocks **coronet**
hind tendons   **gaskin**
cheek   **crest**
chestnut

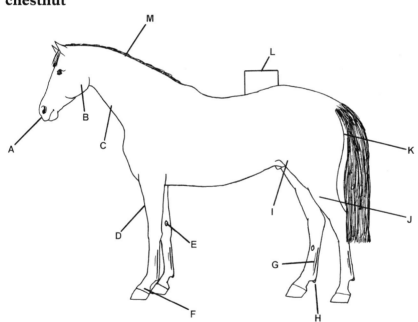

9 Cross out the wrong words to make the sentence correct.

A horse's *front/hind* feet are *rounder/squarer* than his *hind/front* feet and should slope at an angle of 44° to 50°.

10 What is the correct term for a horse which turns its toes inwards?

a) Pigeon-toed. ☐

b) Crow-toed. ☐

c) Penguin-toed. ☐

11 Can you explain what 'deep through the girth' means?

_____

_____

12 Draw on the diagram where you think the horse's heart should be.

13 Join up the sentences.

a) A cold-backed horse   **i)** is one that dips his back when mounted.

b) A roached-back horse   **ii)** is one whose back dips significantly downwards.

c) A hollow-backed horse   **ii)** is one whose back curves upwards.

14 What are tendons?

a) They are cords extending from the muscles, which then attach to the bones. ☐

b) They are ligaments which protect the bones from injury. ☐

c) They are vessels which carry a blood supply to the bones. ☐

15 Name the horse's five senses?

1 _____ 2 _____ 3 _____
4 _____ 5 _____

Watering and feeding

16 Of these grasses, which four are preferable to the others for making up good grazing?

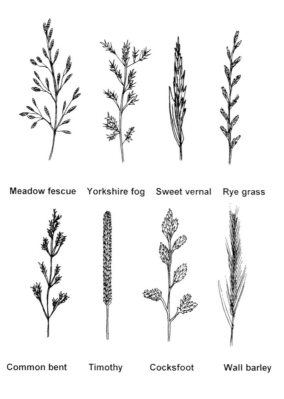

Meadow fescue   Yorkshire fog   Sweet vernal   Rye grass

Common bent   Timothy   Cocksfoot   Wall barley

_____

_____

17 A horse will drink water more readily if it has been left to stand for a few hours, rather than if it has come straight from the tap.   true ☐   false ☐

18 The temperature outside is -5°C. Your horse is living out in the field and you notice that his water trough is frozen over. What do you do?

a) Nothing as horses will break ice with their teeth to get a drink when thirsty.   ☐

b) Break the ice and remove it, repeating this procedure three times a day.   ☐

c) Pour boiling water into the trough every night.   ☐

19 In his natural environment the horse will eat little and often. What term is used to describe this type of feeding pattern?

a) Dribble feeding.   ☐

b) Random feeding.   ☐

c) Trickle feeding.   ☐

20 Would you say that this was a good height at which to hang a haynet?   yes ☐   no ☐

21 Cross out the wrong words to make the sentence correct.
An adult horse's body comprises *60–70%/30–40% water/fats* so it is possible that a *20%/80%* loss of *fats/water* will prove fatal.

22 The condition of a horse reflects whether he is being fed correctly according to his work, temperament and weight. However, other factors may also affect his overall well-being. Can you name four other influencing factors:

1 _____ 2 _____
3 _____ 4 _____

23 What has to be done to whole barley or linseed before it can be fed?

a) It has to be soaked for 24 hours. ☐

b) It has to be soaked and properly cooked. ☐

c) Nothing, it can be fed raw. ☐

24 Here you can see three different forms of a foodstuff for horses. **A)** is the whole plant; **B)** is processed cubes; **C)** is processed pulp. What is the feed? _____

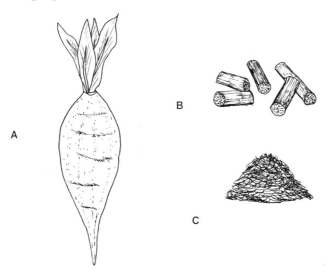

A

B

C

25 Which sentences are true of this feed.

a) It must be soaked for 24 hours before feeding.

b) It must be soaked in its own volume again of water.

c) After soaking, it should be fed within 48 hours, or 24 hours during warm weather.

d) It is one of the best 'straight' feeds for increasing body weight. The true sentences are: _____

Health care and veterinary knowledge

26 What figures would give *cause for concern* when taking the horse's temperature, pulse and respiration while at rest?

Temperature: **a)** 100.5°F ☐ **b)** 95.5°F ☐ **c)** 105.5°F ☐

Pulse (beats per minute): **a)** 80–86 ☐ **b)** 36–42 ☐ **c)** 50–56 ☐

Respiration breaths/pm: **a)** 12 ☐ **b)** 24 ☐ **c)** 48 ☐

27 What type of wound is a gall?

a) It is a wound caused by one horse kicking another while wearing shoes. ☐

b) It is a wound caused by something burning the horse. ☐

c) It is a wound caused by rubbing tack. ☐

28 This condition is characterised by the horse 'pointing' one or other front foot as is seen on page 13. When the horse moves, he will place his foot down toe first, in order to avoid pressure on the area affected by this condition. Usually, the first thing noticed about the condition is that the horse becomes lame. What is the condition?

_____

29 Four principal steps are usually followed in the treatment of wounds. Can you name them in the correct order?

1 _____

2 _____

3 _____

4 _____

30 What word, beginning with the letter *T*, is a method of treating an injured foot or limb by placing the affected part directly into a container of hand-hot or cold water. T_____

31 Fill in the missing words.

a) A _____ is a split in the hoof wall, running downwards from the coronet.

b) A _____ is a bruise of the sole in the region of the heel, lying just under the heel of the shoe.

c) An _____ is a wound on the bulb of the heel of the front foot, caused by the hind foot striking into it.

32 As you can see, this horse's glands are enlarged. He also has a thick discharge from the nostrils, seems to have difficulty in swallowing and his temperature has risen to 106°F. What do you think might be wrong with him?

_____

_____

33 Is the above condition contagious?

a) Yes, highly contagious. ☐

b) Not at all. ☐

c) It is slightly contagious, but two horses would actually have to sniff each other for it to be passed over. ☐

34 How often should a horse's teeth be checked by a qualified person?

a) Once a month. ☐

b) Every six months. ☐

c) Every year. ☐

35 Worming should be carried out approximately every six to eight weeks.   true ☐   false ☐

Psychology

36 This horse is obviously a nice type, but can you point out three reasons why you would not mind approaching him?

1 _____

2 _____

3 _____

37 What is the horse's principal method of self-preservation?

a) Flight. ☐

b) Fight. ☐

c) Cunning. ☐

38 The horse's sight does not adapt quickly from light to dark, or vice versa, so he is naturally afraid of dark places.
true ☐   false ☐

39 Can a horse learn to understand human language?

a) No, he can only recognise familiar words and responds more to the tone of voice than to specific words. ☐

b) Yes, once he learns a word he will respond correctly to it, whoever is talking. ☐

c) Yes, he can actually understand what is being said, even if he is not being spoken to directly. ☐

40 It is often thought that this habit develops out of boredom, although it has also been linked to digestive problems. What exactly is the habit, and what may it lead to?

_____

_____

_____

The foot and shoeing

41 What is the art of shoeing?

a) To make the shoe fit the foot. ☐

b) To make the foot fit the shoe. ☐

c) To make sure the foot does not crack up when shoes are applied. ☐

42 There are three exterior parts of a hoof, what are they?

1 _____

2 _____

3 _____

43 Can you name three indications that a horse needs re-shoeing?

1 ——————————————————————————————

2 ——————————————————————————————

3 ——————————————————————————————

44 What do you think is wrong with this horse's foot.

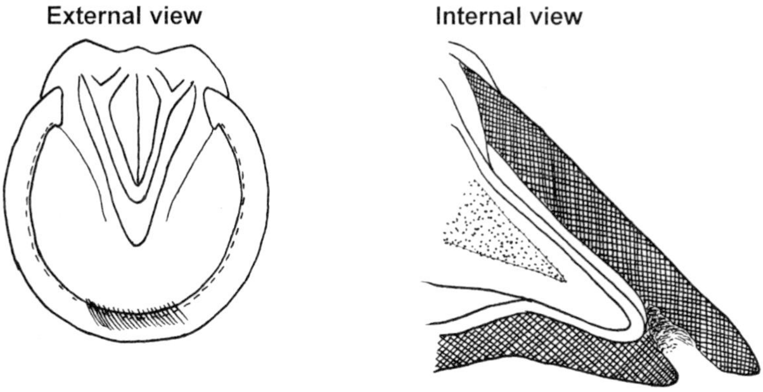

External view   Internal view

a) He has a condition known as seedy toe. ☐

b) He has a condition known as laminitis. ☐

c) He has a condition known as sand cracks. ☐

45 Would you expect the horse to be lame from the above condition?

a) Not unless it has become infected. ☐

b) Yes, the horse would be extremely lame. ☐

c) Only if the horse was ridden. ☐

46 What type of shoe beginning with the letter *F* is used to help prevent brushing? F_____

47 Which of the following are systems of shoeing currently in practice?

a) Hot shoeing   yes ☐   no ☐

b) Burn shoeing   yes ☐   no ☐

c) Freeze shoeing   yes ☐   no ☐

d) Cold shoeing   yes ☐   no ☐

48 Can you name the farrier's tools?

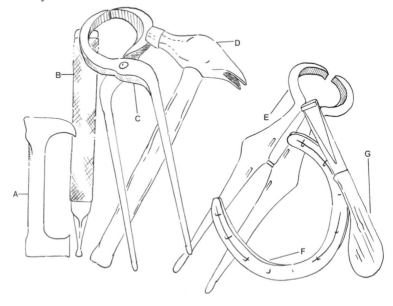

A _____   **B** _____   **C** _____
D _____   **E** _____   **F** _____
G _____

49 What part of the foot bears most of the horse's weight?

a) The frog. ☐

b) The sole. ☐

c) The wall. ☐

50 Give an explanation why new nails should not be knocked into old nail holes.

_____

_____

_____

The stabled horse/stable design

51 What is the 'ideal' size for a stable doorway?

a) 2.4 m (8 ft) high and 1.2 m (4 ft) wide. ☐

b) 2 m (6½ ft) high and 2.1 m (7 ft) wide. ☐

c) 1.2 m (4 ft) high and 2.4 m (8 ft) wide. ☐

52 Explain why some roofs are designed in this way.

_____

_____

53 Stable drains should have a slope of 1:60 towards either the front or back of the stable.   true ☐   false ☐

54 At what height would you fix a ring at the back of a stable for tying up a horse?

a) 2 m (6½ ft).   ☐

b) 1.5 m (5 ft).   ☐

c) 1 m (3 ft).   ☐

55 What is the missing word?

A _____-_____ system on the electrical circuit is essential so that the electric current will be cut off immediately if any fault in the wiring or machinery in use occurs.

56 What is this fitting to a stable door used for?

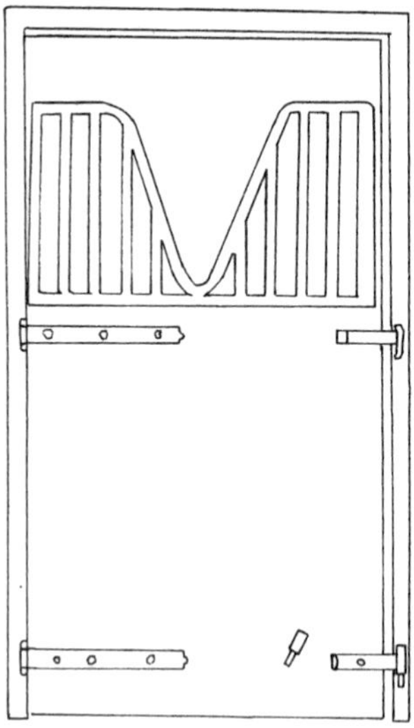

a) It prevents the horse from jumping out over the top door.   ☐

b) It prevents the horse from weaving.   ☐

c) It prevents the horse from biting passersby.   ☐

57 Join up the sentences.

a) Barley straw   **i)** is highly palatable to horses and easily becomes saturated.

b) Wheat straw   **ii)** is of a bright colour and usually fairly long.

c) Oat straw   **iii)** can have a short stalk and become's brittle when heavily compacted.

58 What is meant by DIY livery?

_____

_____

59 If you are keeping a horse on a deep litter system, what must you ensure is kept scrupulously clean?

a) His rugs. ☐

b) His sheath. ☐

c) His feet. ☐

60 Why might a horse be tied up in this way?

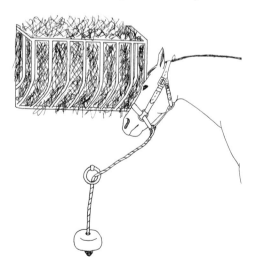

a) Because it stops him from pulling back and breaking his head-collar. ☐

b) Because it prevents him from turning round and biting you as you enter his stable. ☐

c) Because it allows him to lie down in a stall without getting his legs tangled up in the lead rope. ☐

The horse at grass

61 You should avoid excessive grooming of a horse which lives out.   true ☐   false ☐

62 Which sentence best describes your reason for answering the last question as you did?

a) Excessive grooming removes the grease from the horse's coat, which is his natural protection against rain and cold weather. ☐

b) Excessive grooming is not harmful to the horse and actually prevents ringworm and sweet itch. ☐

c) Excessive grooming will make the horse's coat fall out. ☐

63 Four horses are living together in a field during the winter. Their owner supplies them with hay morning and night. How many piles of hay should she be providing each time?

_____

64 Some of these plants are poisonous, while others can be beneficial to the horse. Can you sort them out?

Foxglove is	poisonous ☐	beneficial ☐
Dandelion is	poisonous ☐	beneficial ☐
Acorns are	poisonous ☐	beneficial ☐

Garlic is   poisonous ☐   beneficial ☐

Ragwort is   poisonous ☐   beneficial ☐

Yew is   poisonous ☐   beneficial ☐

Foxglove

Dandelion

Acorns

Garlic

Ragwort

Yew

65 Is there a rule that says 'one acre, one horse'?

_____

_____

66 What name is given to the system of grazing when sheep or cattle are used to clean up a paddock because they will graze areas rejected by a horse? The system is known as: _____

67 What type of 'fence' is the safest choice for enclosing a horse's paddock?

a) A hedge.   ☐

b) Electric fencing.   ☐

c) Pig/sheep netting.   ☐

68 Here we can see two designs for field shelters. One design is more suitable when more than one horse is occupying a field. Which one is it?

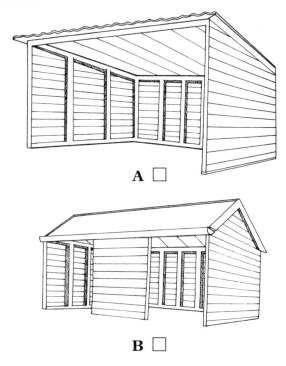

A ☐

B ☐

69 Give the reasons for your answer above: _____
_____
_____

70 Out of the following list, which three would provide an ideal water source from a stream?

firm approach   a bank   gravelled bottom

sandy bottom   running water   still water

shallow   deep

The ideal stream would be one with: _____
_____

Horse clothing

71 What is the best type of protection a horse can have?

a) His natural coat. ☐

b) A thick, quilted night rug. ☐

c) A waterproof rug. ☐

72 Which shows the correct way to fasten the hind leg straps of a New Zealand rug?

A ☐

B ☐

C ☐

73 Cross out the wrong words to make the sentence correct.

Rugs with *crossover surcingles/rollers* are preferable to ones with *crossover surcingles/rollers* as they do not put any extra pressure on the *spine/tummy*.

74 With what should all exercise sheets be fitted?

a) A fillet string. ☐

b) A girth strap. ☐

c) A sweat band. ☐

75 Give the reasons for your answer: _____

_____

_____

76 As a quick measurement, to determine its length a rug is measured from the front chest straps to the back edge of the rug. Which other three measurements would you take to ensure an optimum fit? On the diagram, draw on the measurements you would take.

77 What might you use to prevent a known rug tearer from ripping his rug?

a) A bib. ☐

b) A crib-strap. ☐

c) A muzzle. ☐

78 What word, beginning with the letter *B*, is attached to the D-rings on a roller to stop the roller from slipping backwards?
B_____

79 In relation to horse rugs, what is meant by the term 'breathable'?

a) It means that the rug will allow the passage of air. ☐

b) It means that the rug will ensure a layer of oxygen around the horse's body. ☐

c) It means that the rug has oxygen impregnated into its fibres. ☐

80 This diagram shows the correct way to put on an under-blanket. Name three common mistakes that are often made during fitting, which would leave underblankets liable to slipping.

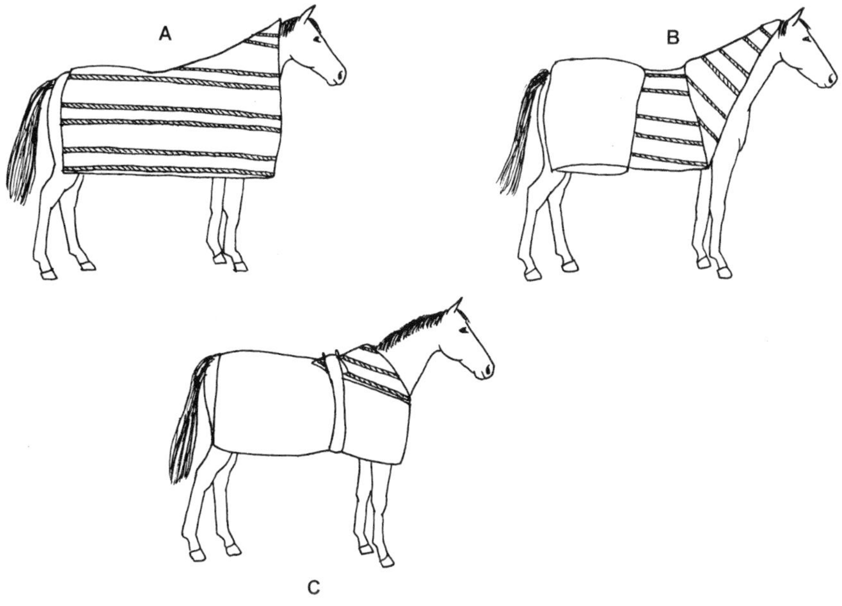

1 _____

2 _____

3 _____

Travelling

81 What item, beginning with the letter *P*, is used to protect the horse's head while travelling? P_____

82 What type of boot is used when travelling a horse?

a) A sausage boot. ☐

b) An equiboot. ☐

c) A hock boot. ☐

83 Which four main areas do you need to protect when travelling the horse?

1 ———————————————————————

2 ———————————————————————

3 ———————————————————————

4 ———————————————————————

84 Which of these boots will help to protect a horse's knees while travelling?

A ☐   B ☐

C ☐

85 How should a horse be tied during travelling?

a) He should be tied up fairly short. ☐

b) He should not be tied at all. ☐

c) He should be tied fairly loose. ☐

86 If you were loading a single horse into a double trailer with a partition, on which side would you put him in the UK?
On the left side because: _____

_____

On the right side because: _____

_____

87 As a general rule, roughly how much room should there be between the horse and the partition on each side?

a) About 30 cm (1 ft) on each side. ☐

b) About 15 cm (6 in) on each side. ☐

c) There should be no room between the horse and the partition. ☐

88 Bearing in mind that this leg protector is fitted to the off-side hind leg, can you comment upon its fitting?

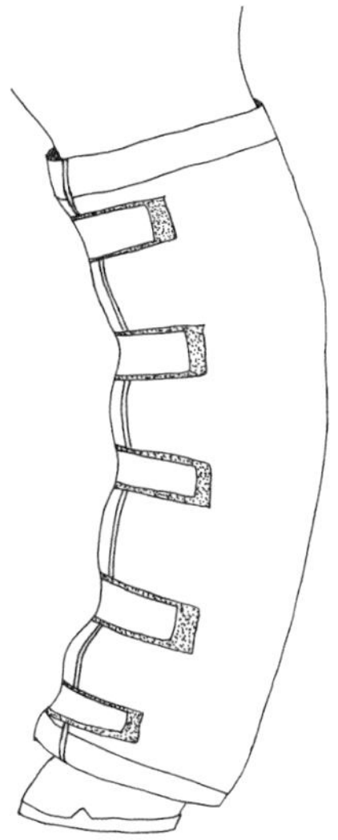

_____

_____

_____

89 Your horse has been loaded into your trailer many times but he can, on occasion, be a little stubborn. On one particular day, your usual efforts at coaxing him in do not work. What do you do?

a) Tack him up and ride him in. ☐

b) Smack him on the rump with a lungeing whip. ☐

c) Draw a lungeing rein up from behind, above his hocks. ☐

90 If unloading a horse from a front-unload trailer, you should untie the horse before lifting the front bar. true ☐ false ☐

Clipping, trimming and turnout

91 Where would you use a wisp?

a) On the horse's head. ☐

b) On the mane and tail. ☐

c) Over the horse's muscles. ☐

92 Name these types of clip.

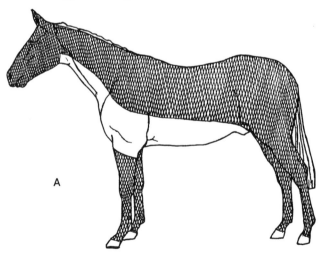

A

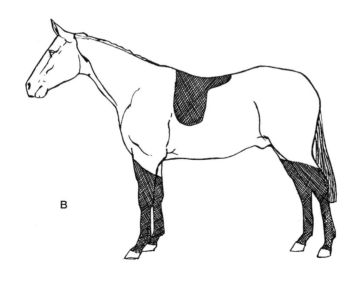

A _____.

B _____.

93 To what type of horse would you give clip A and what type would clip B most suit?

_____

_____

_____

94 Explain why you might rub Vaseline into a horse's heels before washing his legs in winter?

_____

_____

95 Name three reasons why horses are clipped:

1 _____

2 _____

3 _____

96 Does this show the correct way to trim up a horse's legs?

a) Yes, it is safe and will not leave ridges in the hair. ☐

b) No, it is not safe as you could cut your hands. ☐

c) No, it will leave ridges in the hair. ☐

97 What word, beginning with the letter *H*, describes the complete removal of the mane with clippers? H_____

98 What are 'cat hairs'?

a) Silky hairs which grow a different colour to the clipped coat.
☐

b) Spiky hair which grows along the top of a poorly clipped mane. ☐

c) Long, untidy hairs which grow around the face after clipping.
☐

99 There are four main reasons why you would pull a horse's mane. Two reasons are to help the mane lie flat and to make it easier to plait. What are the other two?

a) _____

b) _____

100 Is this horse correctly plaited?   yes ☐   no ☐

Why?

PART 2

Riding and schooling

Safety with horses

101 What is meant by the term 'defensive riding'?

a) It means riding directly at anything which startles the horse. ☐

b) It means anticipating what might happen and so taking up a position in the road where you can be seen clearly. ☐

c) It means riding on the opposite side of the road so that a car will have to slow down if it wants to overtake. ☐

102 A ride of six horses is about to set out from the riding school. There are three novice riders, three experienced riders, five traffic-proof horses and one young horse. How should they be arranged in the interests of safety?

_____

_____

_____

103 When riding one horse and leading another, on which side should the led horse be?

a) On the off side of the ridden horse. ☐

b) On the near side of the ridden horse. ☐

c) There must be enough rein so that the led horse can follow on behind the ridden horse. ☐

104 Can you explain what is happening here?

_____

_____

_____

105 In which hand should you carry a whip when riding on the roads?   left ☐   right ☐   no whip should be carried ☐

106 Road signs that give warnings are triangular.
true ☐   false ☐

107 If you came upon a stationary lorry which, despite all your efforts, your horse would not go past, what would you do?

a) Get off and lead him. ☐

b) Turn around and go back the way you came. ☐

c) Ask the lorry driver to move the vehicle. ☐

35

108 This rider has just mounted. Should she be doing this?

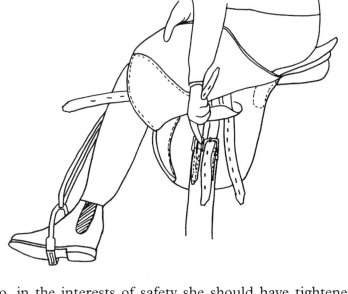

a) No, in the interests of safety she should have tightened her girth before mounting. ☐

b) Yes, in the interests of safety the girth should always be tightened after mounting as well as before. ☐

c) It really does not matter when the girth is tightened, as long as it is tightened. ☐

109 What is it essential that you do before giving any road signal?

_____

_____

110 You are in a car and come up behind a rider who is waving her right arm slowly up and down. What do you do?

a) Slow down. ☐

b) Overtake. ☐

c) Turn around and find an alternative route. ☐

Tack

111 Which is more severe?

a) A bit with a thin mouthpiece. ☐

b) A bit with a thick mouthpiece. ☐

112 When selecting an appropriate bit for use, you should consider what effect it will have inside the horse's mouth. Can you name the internal parts of a horse's mouth?

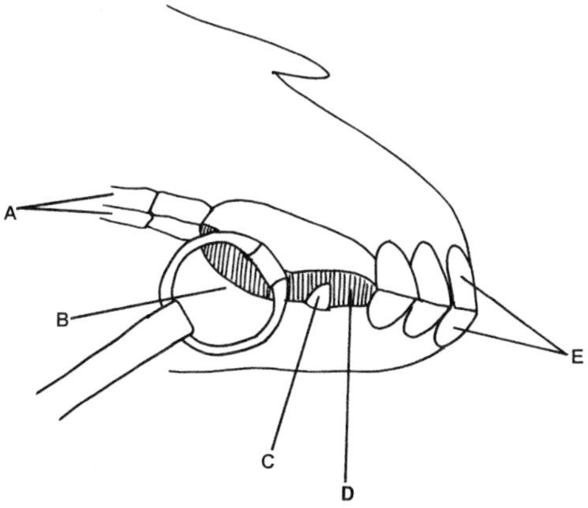

A _____ B _____ C _____
D _____ E _____

113 Take another look at the diagram above. Would you say this bit was sitting in the right place?

a) No, it is too low and could interfere with the front teeth. ☐

b) No, it should not be resting on the tongue like this. ☐

c) Yes, it is sitting neatly on the tongue and will not interfere with either back or front teeth. ☐

114 What word, beginning with the letter *W*, is the most common type of curb bit? W _____

115 Join up the sentences.

a) A Grakle   **i)**   is similar to a cavesson noseband but has another strap which fixes under the bit rings.

b) A drop   **ii)**   consists of two straps which go around the horse's nose in a figure-of-eight design.

c) A flash   **iii)**   has the front band sitting a few inches above the nostril and the back band fastened under the bit rings.

116 Can you name the parts of this snaffle bridle?

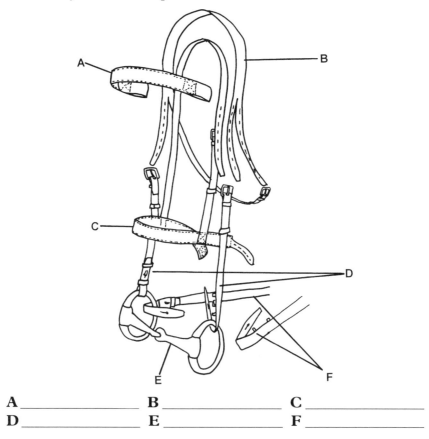

A_____	B_____	C_____
D_____	E_____	F_____

117 Fill in the missing words from the list below.

The purpose of a _____ is to _____ the horse from _____ his head above the level of _____.

martingale	**lifting**
flexion	**cavesson**
bib	**control**
prevent	**safety**
encourage	**rearing**

118 What word, begging with the letter *A*, is being discussed?

As well as holding the saddle in place this item of tack is specially shaped so that it will prevent chafing behind the horse's elbow.

A_____

119 What sort of stirrup irons are the best?

a) Nickel ones, which have a large foot hole. ☐

b) Heavy, stainless steel ones. ☐

c) Light, stainless steel ones. ☐

120 Name the different types of saddle.

A

B

C

A _____

B _____

C _____

Schooling methods

121 What is the item of tack, worn on the horse's head, to which the lunge rein is attached?

a) Lungeing cavesson. ☐

b) Lungeing flash. ☐

c) Lungeing bridle. ☐

122 What is the system of schooling when the horses is free from any physical contact with the trainer?

_____

123 When a horse is asked to halt on the lunge, should he:

a) Be expected to stand still out on the circle. ☐

b) Be expected to turn in and face his trainer. ☐

c) Be expected to walk in and halt at his trainer's side. ☐

124 Which trainer is standing in the best position for normal lungeing? **A** ☐ **B** ☐

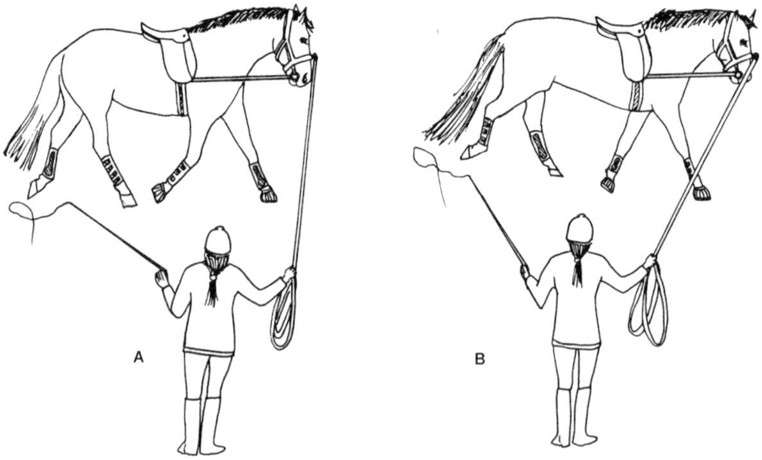

125 Give the reasons for your answer to question 124.

_____

_____

126 Cross out the wrong words to make the sentence correct.

Two _twenty-/ten-minute_ sessions are of greater value than _four/one ten/twenty minute_ session/s when schooling a young horse.

127 Mouthing is the procedure which teaches the horse the feel and action of the bit.   true ☐   false ☐

128 This method of schooling is called 'line reining' and is used to teach the horse manners.   true ☐   false ☐

129 Control of the horse on the lunge is gained through what three things?

1 _____ 2 _____ 3 _____

130 When lungeing, what items of tack are often used which run from the saddle or roller to the bit?

a) Long reins. ☐

b) Facet reins. ☐

c) Side reins. ☐

Riding technique

131 Does the term 'heels down, toes in' correctly describe a good foot position?   yes ☐   no ☐

132 What is this technique called and why is it done?

a) It is called 'playing with the rein' and serves to make the horse alert before moving off. ☐

b) It is called 'jigging' and stops the horse from jog-trotting out on a ride. ☐

c) It is called 'rein-stopping' and prevents the horse from getting his tongue over the bit. ☐

133 What word, beginning with the letter *I*, is created by putting more vigour into the horse's movement? I_____

134 On what diagonal should you always be sitting when in rising trot?

a) Inside diagonal. ☐

b) Outside diagonal. ☐

c) Centre diagonal. ☐

135 To change the diagonal down the centre line, you would sit for two beats, before rising again.   true ☐   false ☐

136 Comment upon the way in which this rider is handling a rearing horse.

_____

_____

_____

137 What should the rider do next?

a) Jump off. ☐

b) As soon as the horse comes down, straighten up and kick the horse onwards firmly. ☐

c) As soon as the horse comes down, jump off. ☐

138 From the list below fill in the missing words. (Words may be used once, twice or not at all.)

To ask a horse to turn right, you would first place your _____ leg on the _____ and your _____ leg behind the _____. Then you would apply a little _____ on the _____ rein by pulling it back about _____ or so, so that the horse feels the _____ moving in his mouth.

centre	**pressure**
right	**half an inch**
saddle	**four inches**
girth	**bit**
left	**rein**
snatch	

139 Which of these sentences are true?

a) If you continually jab your horse in the mouth he will stop 'listening' to your rein aids. ☐

b) If you continually 'niggle' with your feet on your horse's sides, he will start to ignore your leg aids. ☐

c) If you continually 'give' the rein when your horse takes the bit, he will remain responsive to your aids. ☐

140 Would you say this rider has a good technique for riding down hills?

a) Yes, she is leaning forwards to stay over the horse's centre of gravity. ☐

b) No, she is in danger of falling off if the horse stumbles, which he is more likely to do as her weight is too far forward and is unbalancing him. ☐

c) Yes, she has the reins tight enough so that she can hold the horse up if he trips or stumbles. ☐

Gaits

141 What word is missing?

A _____ is the entire cycle of motion in which all four legs fulfil their movement and thus propel the horse forward.

142 When the horse moves in any gait he uses every muscle in his body.   true ☐   false ☐

143 Which of the horse's muscles provide his pushing power?

a) The muscles of the hindquarters. ☐

b) The muscles of the forequarters. ☐

c) The muscles of the neck. ☐

144 Here we can see a sequence of footfalls within a gait. What is the gait?

a) Trot. ☐

b) Canter. ☐

c) Gallop. ☐

145 Why is it essential that the horse has enough freedom to move his head and neck as required, in harmony with the rest of his body.

_____

_____

146 What is meant by the term 'variations within a gait'?

_____

_____

147 At what speed (approximately) does a horse travel during an ordinary walk?

a) 6 kmph (4 mph). ☐

b) 9.5 kmph (6 mph). ☐

c) 16 kmph (10 mph). ☐

148 This horse is showing various types of trot. Can you say which is which from those given below and opposite?

A

B

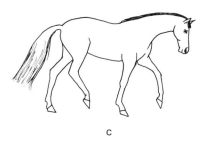

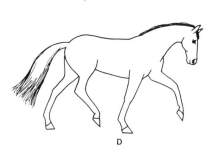

working trot	park trot
extended trot	collected trot
jog trot	rising trot
medium trot	racing trot

A _____   B _____
C _____   D _____

149 What gait is being discussed? 'Two hoof beats are heard, with the legs moving alternately in diagonal pairs, separated by a moment of suspension'. _____.

150 What is the horse's 'balancer'?

a) His quarters. ☐

b) His head and neck. ☐

c) His hooves. ☐

Transitions

151 What is meant by 'progressive' transitions?

a) That the horse goes through the gaits in order to get to the required gait (from walk, through trot to canter, for instance). ☐

47

b) Skipping a gait in order to get to the required gait (such as from walk straight to canter). ☐

c) That the horse runs into the next gait. ☐

152 Here we can see a transition in action. Can you say what two gaits are involved?

_____

153 What is the difference between an upward and downward transition?

_____
_____
_____

154 What should you do during a transition?

a) Lean forwards. ☐

b) Lean backwards. ☐

c) Stay in balance. ☐

155 What three things do transitions test in horse and rider?

suppleness   **rider's skill**
fitness   **physical development**
responsiveness   **intelligence**
rider's talent

1 _____ 2 _____ 3 _____

Fitness work

156 This is the moment of suspension during a gallop. Is the horse inhaling or exhaling at this point?
inhaling ☐   exhaling ☐

157 Why is this moment of suspension important when checking to see if a horse is sound in his wind?

a) Because this is the point when any abnormal respiratory noises may be heard.   ☐

b) Because the horse blows out at this point and this is when he would cough.   ☐

c) Because there would be an absence of any noise at this point if the horse were unsound in his wind.   ☐

158 Why is hillwork of great benefit during fitness training?

a) Because it makes the horse work harder and saves the strain on the front legs. ☐

b) Because it stretches the horse's muscles to their full extent and so prevents injury. ☐

c) Because it means the rider does not have to work so hard to get the horse to do fast work. ☐

159 What does the initial stage of fitness work, known as conditioning, consist of?

_____

_____

160 Is this rider in a good position for fast work?
yes ☐ no ☐

161 Can you give three reasons for your answer to the question above?

1 _____

2 _____

3 _____

162 For the horse to gain some benefit from exercise, some stress must be exerted on his body.   true ☐   false ☐

163 What piece of equipment is it sensible for the unfit horse to wear while undertaking road work?

a) Knee pads.　　　　　　　　　　　　　　　　☐

b) Hock boots.　　　　　　　　　　　　　　　　☐

c) Overreach boots.　　　　　　　　　　　　　　☐

164 Here we can see some common injuries which are often sustained by young or unfit horses when they are starting faster work. Can you name the types of injury?

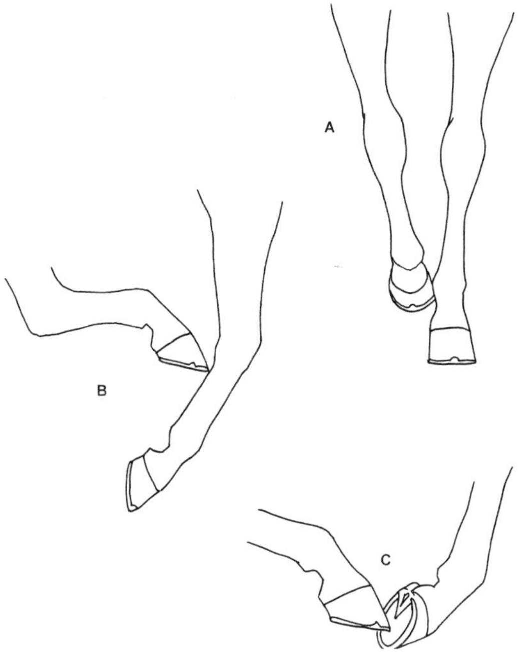

A _____

B _____

C _____

165 What word, beginning with the letter *I*, is a system of training in which the horse is stressed, allowed partially to recover and then stressed again? I_____.

The country code

166 Can a horse and rider be considered to be trespassing if riding around the edge of a farmer's field.

a) Yes. As the farmer owns the land, anyone should get permission before going on it. ☐

b) No. Horses are classed as natural animals and, as such, are allowed to go wherever their rider takes them. ☐

c) They would only be trespassing if the field were fenced off. ☐

167 What is a RUPP and why is it important to riders?

_____
_____
_____

168 Would you say this rider is attempting to open the gate correctly during a ride?

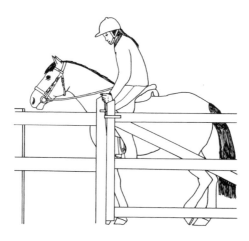

a) No, she should have dismounted ☐

b) No, she should have the horse's head over the gate so that he can help to push it open once the catch has been freed. ☐

c) Yes, she has the horse in the right position so that he cannot barge through the gate once opened. ☐

169 If it has rained heavily during the past few days what should you not do?

_____

_____

170 If you are given permission to ride over a farmer's land, or if a bridleway runs parallel to his land, what two things must you always ensure?

1 _____

2 _____

Group riding

171 If a large group of riders is riding on the roads how should they be arranged?

a) Split into smaller groups of no more than six horses riding in pairs. ☐

b) As one large group riding in single file. ☐

c) As one large group riding in pairs. ☐

172 If you find your horse getting too close to the one in front, while engaged in a group lesson, what would you do in order to avoid a collision?

a) Slow your horse down by pulling on the reins. ☐

b) Ask the rider in front to speed up a bit. ☐

c) Turn out of the line and rejoin the rear of the ride. ☐

173 What is the 'school rule' being practised here?

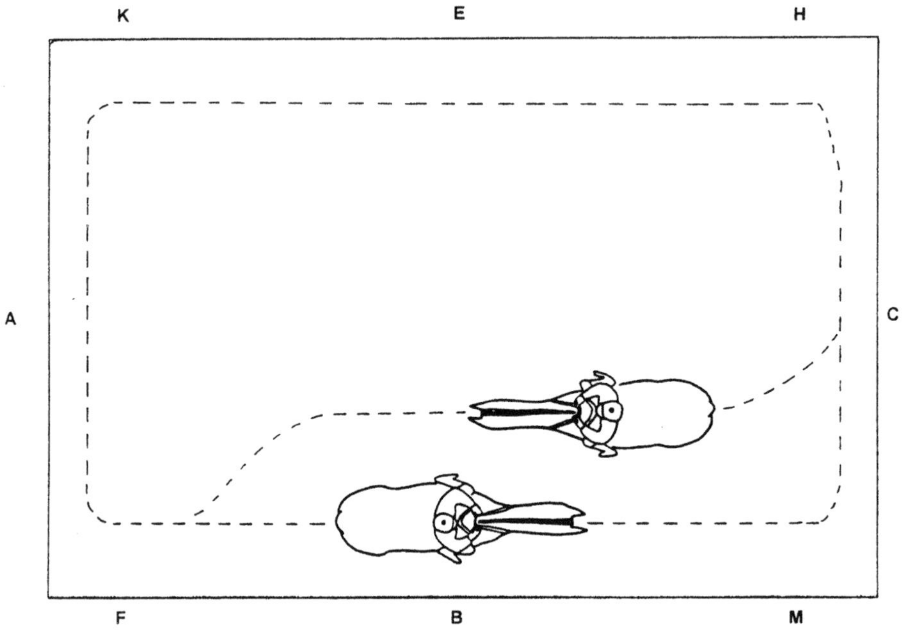

_____

_____

_____

174 What word, beginning with the letter *W*, is used to describe a group of riders making a turn together in the school. W_____

175 What do the riders performing the above manoeuvre have to do in order to ensure they keep in 'line abreast'?

_____

_____

_____

176 What distance should be left between these horses in a group ride in the school?

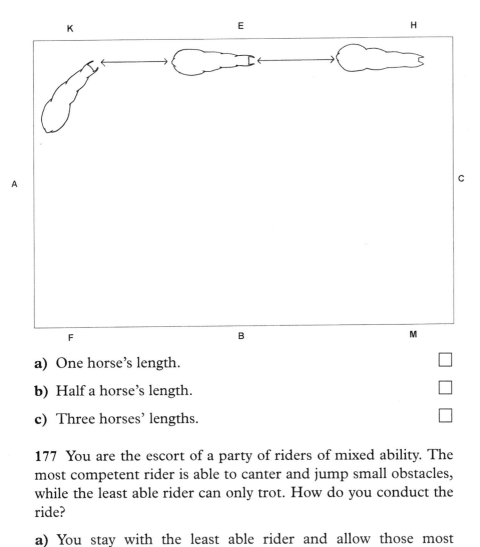

a) One horse's length. ☐

b) Half a horse's length. ☐

c) Three horses' lengths. ☐

177 You are the escort of a party of riders of mixed ability. The most competent rider is able to canter and jump small obstacles, while the least able rider can only trot. How do you conduct the ride?

a) You stay with the least able rider and allow those most experienced to canter off in front of you ☐

b) You encourage the less able rider to have a go at cantering. ☐

c) You keep the whole ride at walk and trot. ☐

178 Fill in the missing words: The horse's natural _____ to be with other horses can work to our _____ in some circumstances, especially when we require one horse to _____ and _____ another's _____.

desire	**follow**
aversion	**opposite**
dislike	**copy**
advantage	**feelings**
detriment	**independent**
handicap	**actions**

179 When a group of riders is on the road, who should give the signals?

---

180 Here we can see an older horse on the outside of a younger horse being taken out on the roads for the first time. Which of these sentences correctly describes the situation?

a) The older horse should be on the inside, so that the younger one can experience traffic coming past. ☐

b) The older horse is preventing the younger horse from swinging its quarters out into the line of traffic should it shy at something along the roadside. ☐

c) The older horse should be in front of the younger horse, so that he learns to take a lead. ☐

d) The rider on the older horse should have the younger horse on a leading rein. ☐

Emergency action

181 What is known as the ABC of an accident?

A is for: _____

_____

B is for: _____

_____

C is for: _____

_____

182 If you come across a rider who has had a fall and is complaining of back pain, or pain in the region of the neck, what should you assume?

a) That their back or neck has been broken. ☐

b) That they may have cut their back or neck. ☐

c) That they may have jarred their back or neck. ☐

183 Why is it essential to lie an unconscious rider on their side in the recovery position?

_____

184 Which rider is acting safely?

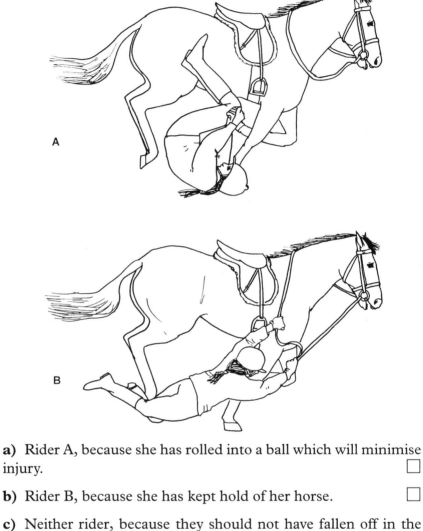

A

B

a) Rider A, because she has rolled into a ball which will minimise injury. ☐

b) Rider B, because she has kept hold of her horse. ☐

c) Neither rider, because they should not have fallen off in the first place. ☐

185 If you arrive at the scene of an accident, the very first thing you should do is to try to find the loose horse.
true ☐   false ☐

186 If you know you are the cause of an accident, should you accept liability?   yes ☐   no ☐

187 Give the reason for your answer to question 186.

_____

_____

_____

188 This rider has had a fall and appears to be unconscious. The first person on the scene is checking for a pulse.

a) Is this the best place to check for a pulse?

_____

_____

b) Should the rider's hat have been removed?

_____

_____

189 What number should you call in order to have a local vet attend the accident scene?

a) 999   ☐

b) 100   ☐

c) 192   ☐

190 Fill in the missing word. If a horse has been involved in an accident, but appears unhurt, he could still be suffering from

_____.

Jumping

191 A jump over an obstacle is simply a longer and higher canter stride.   true ☐   false ☐

192 Can you comment on the rider's position over the fence?

_____

_____

193 Why is jumping training best started from trot?

a) Because the horse can jump higher out of trot. ☐

b) Because it discourages the horse from rushing. ☐

c) Because the horse does not become fatigued as quickly as when cantering. ☐

194 What word, beginning with the letter _G_, is a series of obstacles in a straight line with related distances between them?
G _____

195 What is the purpose of circling a young horse in front of a fence?

a) It enables the horse to be rebalanced before jumping the obstacle. ☐

b) It prevents the horse from refusing. ☐

c) It improves the horse's chances of jumping the fence. ☐

196 What are the five stages of a horse's jump, as seen here?

A _____   B _____

C _____   D _____

E _____

197 Fill in the missing words. Deciding on the right moment to jump is governed by the rider's ability to _____ a _____. Many riders find this very difficult and it is something which only comes through practice and experience.

198 What is a 'bounce' fence?

a) Where the horse does not take a stride in between two fences. ☐

b) Where the horse takes two bouncy canter strides in between two fences. ☐

c) Where the horse jumps up on to a flat surface and bounces off again. ☐

199 All fences in a show-jumping competition must be capable of being knocked down.   true ☐   false ☐

200 What should be the distance between these poles for the average horse at :

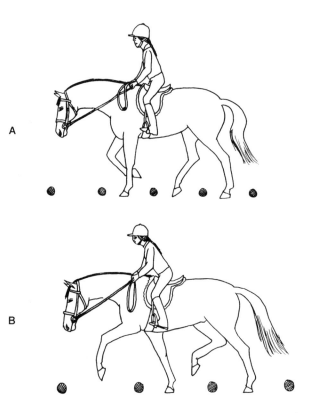

A walk _____   **B** trot _____

Answers

Part 1   Horse management

Anatomy and physical characteristics

1b) Hack, as this is a type of horse, whereas (**a**) and (**c**) are horse colours.

2 This type of head marking is called a white face.

3 a) + iii), **b)** + ii); **c)** + i).

4

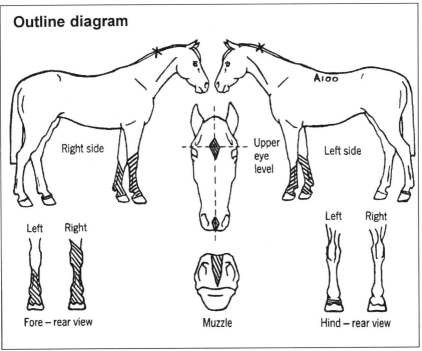

Outline diagram

Right side   Upper eye level   Left side

Left   Right   Left   Right

Fore – rear view   Muzzle   Hind – rear view

5b) They are black marks on a white leg.

6 The term is known as 'bone' – how much 'bone' a horse has is determined by this measurement.

7 a) true;   b) false;   c) true.

8

A	muzzle	**B**	cheek	**C**	windpipe
D	forearm	**E**	chestnut	**F**	coronet
G	hind tendon	**H**	ergot	**I**	stifle
J	gaskin	**K**	point of buttocks	**L**	loins
M	crest				

9 A horse's *front* feet are *rounder* than his *hind* feet and should slope at an angle of 44° to 50°.

10a) Pigeon-toed.

11 Deep through the girth means that the horse has an ample depth to his body from immediately behind the withers down to his tummy line, just behind his elbow (where the girth sits). It is also known as having 'plenty of heart room'.

12

13 a) + i); **b)** + iii); **c)** + ii).

14a) They are cords extending from the muscles which then attach to the bones.

15

1 seeing
2 hearing
3 tasting
4 smelling
5 feeling

Watering and feeding

16 Good grasses are: rye grass, Timothy, cocksfoot and meadow fescue. Wall barley, Yorkshire fog and sweet vernal are of poor nutritional value.

17 False, horses always prefer fresh water.

18b) Break the ice and remove it, repeating this procedure three times a day.

19c) Trickle feeding.

20 Yes, because the horse cannot get his feet caught in it, but it is not so high that seeds will fall into his eyes.

21 An adult horse's body comprises *60–70% water* so it is possible that a *20%* loss of *water* will prove fatal.

22 Any from:
age
climate
type (Arab or cob for instance)
companions (a bullying horse may cause others to lose weight and lack of a companion may cause a horse to pine)
illness
condition of teeth
breeding activity (an in-foal or lactating mare will need special feeding)
parasites (worms will affect condition, for instance)
stable vices (some of these, such as wind sucking, interfere with digestion, while weaving leads to a waste of energy)

23b) Both have to be soaked and properly cooked.

24 Sugar beet.

25 a), c) and **d)** are correct. **b)** is incorrect as it must be soaked in at least *twice* its own volume of water.

Health care and veterinary knowledge

26 Those figures which would give cause for concern are:

Temperature: **b)** 95.5°F   **c)** 105.5°F

Pulse (beats per minute):   **a)** 80–86   **c)** 50–56

Respiration breaths/pm: **b)** 24   **c)** 48

27c) It is a wound caused by rubbing tack.

28 Navicular.

29

1 Stop the bleeding – by applying pressure over a clean pad.

2 Clean the wound – by removing foreign matter and then washing.

3 Dress the wound – with an antiseptic power or spray, by using an impregnated dressing or by poulticing, as appropriate.

4 Protect the wound with bandages applied over suitable padding, remembering to allow room for swelling.

30 Tubbing.

31 a) sand-crack;   **b)** corn;   **c)** overreach.

32 He has probably got *strangles*.

33a) Yes, highly contagious.

34b) Every six months.

35 True.

Psychology

36 Any three of the following:

1 Because he has his ears forward.

2 Because he has a nice, kind eye, which is not showing the white.

3 Because he is generally relaxed and calm.

4 Because his teeth are not bared (showing).

37a) Flight.

38 True.

39a) No, he can only recognise familiar words and responds more to the tone of voice rather than specific words.

40 The habit is called crib biting, a vice which would render the horse unsound if vetted. It is when the horse grabs hold of a post or other object, draws in air and swallows it. It can lead to wind-sucking, where the horse learns to suck in air without grabbing hold of any object and so can do it anytime, anywhere.

The foot and shoeing

41a) To make the shoe fit the foot.

42 1 the wall; **2** the sole; **3** the frog.

43 Any of the following:
The clenches have risen and can be seen standing proud of the wall.
The shoe has been lost.
The shoe is loose.
The hoof is long and misshapen.
The shoe has worn thin.

44a) He has seedy toe.

45a) Not unless it has become infected.

46 Feathered shoe.

47 a) hot shoeing and **d)** cold shoeing are current shoeing methods.

48
A buffer	**B** rasp	**C** pincers
D driving hammer	**E** hoof cutters	**F** shoe
G drawing knife		

49c) The wall.

50 Due to pressure from the shoe during use, old nail holes become slightly enlarged and so knocking new nails into old holes will cause the shoes to work loose and be cast far more frequently. It would also weaken the horn considerably, paving the way for cracks in the hoof.

The stabled horse/stable design

51 2.4 m (8 ft) high and 1.2 m (4 ft) wide

52 This is called a ventilator hood. It ensures that the horse has a constant supply of fresh air which is essential if diseases which affect respiration are to be prevented.

53 True.

54b) 1.5 m (5 ft).

55 Trip-switch.

56b) It prevents the horse from weaving.

57 a) + ii); **b)** + iii); **c)** + i).

58 DIY livery means Do It Yourself livery where you rent a stable and use of a paddock but take care of your horse's needs yourself.

59c) His feet.

60c) Because it allows him to lie down in a stall without getting his legs tangled up in the lead rope.

The horse at grass

61 True.

62a) Excessive grooming removes the grease from the horse's coat, which is his natural protection against rain and cold weather.

63 Five piles. You should always ensure that there is a 'spare' pile to prevent horses from squabbling.

64 Foxglove, acorns, ragwort and yew are poisonous. Dandelions and garlic are beneficial.

65 No. While four acres will be sufficient for four horses, because there is some crossover between horses and scope for paddock management, one acre is not sufficient for a single horse.

66 The system is known as 'mixed' grazing.

67a) A hedge is the safest as a horse cannot get caught in it nor put his feet and legs through it as he can with the other two.

68 B.

69 B is more suitable for more than one horse as there are two exits. This will enable a horse to get away from any other which might be bullying it.

70 The ideal stream would be one with a firm approach, a gravelled bottom and running water.

Horse clothing

71a) His natural coat.

72 A is correct. The straps should be linked around each other and fastened again on the same side on which they are attached to the rug.

73 Rugs with *crossover surcingles* are preferable to ones with *rollers* as they do not put any extra pressure on the *spine*.

74a) A fillet string.

75 All exercise sheets should have a fillet string to prevent them from blowing up and over the horse's back in windy conditions.

76

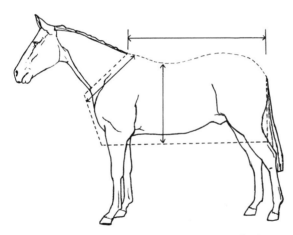

77a) is correct. A crib-strap would not prevent the horse from tearing his rugs. A muzzle would, but it would also prevent the horse from eating and possibly drinking, so is not suitable for this purpose.

78 Breast-girth.

79a) It means that the rug will allow the passage of air.

80 Any of the following are quite usual:

a) The flap might be folded under the top rug.

b) The flap might be folded over the top of the roller.

c) The blanket might not have been folded into a point first, just simply rolled back.

d) The blanket may not have been placed far enough up the horse's neck to start with so the flap would not reach underneath the roller.

Travelling

81 Poll guard.

82c) A hock boot.

83
1 The head – by using a poll guard or cap.
2 The legs – by using boots, leg protectors or bandages.
3 The tail – by using a tail guard or bandages.
4 The body – by using rugs.

84 **B** is correct. Boot **A** is a coronet boot and boot **C** is an overreach boot.

85a) He should be tied up fairly short.

86 On the right side behind the driver. Because of the camber of the road, the middle of the road is usually flatter and so enables the horse to keep its balance better and have a less bumpy ride. (Note: in countries where cars drive on the right-hand side, the horse would be loaded on the left.)

87b) About 15 cm (6 in) on each side.

88 It is not fitted correctly. This leg protector is, in fact, a near-side one because the fastening tapes should always be done up on the outside of the leg, with the tape points facing backwards.

89c) Draw a lungeing rein up from behind, above the hocks.

90 True: this is for safety reasons. If he tries to rush out, he might panic if still tied up.

Clipping, trimming and turnout

91c) Over the horse's muscles.

92 A low trace clip; **B** hunter clip.

93 Clip **A** would generally suit horses in light work which are stabled at night and turned out during the day with a waterproof rug in cold, wet weather. Clip **B** would suit a horse in hard work, who has sensitive skin under the saddle area. This horse would be stabled for much of the time and would certainly only be turned out wearing protective rugs.

94 You would do this to reduce the risk of cracked heels.

95 Any of the following:
a) To enable a horse to work in winter without becoming stressed.
b) To enable the horse to work for longer and faster periods, without affecting the quality of the work.
c) To avoid heavy sweating and so maintain condition.
d) To help the horse to dry quicker after work.
e) To prevent disease.
f) To reduce the time spent on grooming.

96a) Yes, it is safe and will not leave ridges in the hair.

97 Hogging.

98c) Long, untidy hairs which grow around the face after clipping.

99a) To thin out an over-thick mane.   **b)** To reduce the length of a long mane.

100 Yes. The horse is correctly plaited because it is customary to have an uneven number of plaits down the mane with the forelock plait making an even number.

Part 2   Riding and schooling

Safety with horses

101b) It means anticipating what might happen and taking up a position in the road where you can be seen clearly.

102 Each novice rider must be on a traffic-proof horse. At the front of the ride there will be an experienced rider on a traffic-proof horse. Behind him or her, there will be the three novice riders. Behind the novice riders will be the young horse, with an experienced rider, and alongside the young horse there will be the experienced rider on a traffic-proof horse.

103b) On the near side of the ridden horse.

104 The girl has just tightened the girth so she is pulling the front leg forward so that any wrinkles of skin under the girth are pulled flat. This will prevent discomfort during a ride and, ultimately, sores if the skin remains puckered.

105 Right.

106 True.

107a) Get off and lead him.

108b) is correct. Even if you tighten a girth before mounting, the horse may have been blowing out so it is essential to check it and tighten it again after mounting if it requires it.

109 It is essential to look all round to see what traffic or hazards might be about.

110a) Slow down.

Tack

111a) A bit with a thin mouthpiece.

112 A molar teeth; **B** bars; **C** tush; **D** tongue; **E** incisor teeth.

113c) Yes, it is sitting neatly on the tongue and will not interfere with either back or front teeth.

114 Weymouth.

115 a) + ii); **b)** + iii) **c)** + i).

116 A browband; **B** headpiece with attached throatlash; **C** cavesson noseband; **D** cheekpieces; **E** eggbutt snaffle; **F** reins.

117 The purpose of a *martingale* is to *prevent* the horse from *lifting* his head above the level of *control*.

118 Atherstone girth.

119b) Heavy, stainless steel irons are the best as they will hang down well and not follow the foot in the event of a fall.

120 A general or all-purpose saddle; **B** dressage saddle; **C** showjumping or just jumping saddle.

Schooling methods

121a) Lungeing cavesson.

122 Loose schooling.

123a) Be expected to stand still out on the circle.

124 B.

125 Trainer **B** has more control as she is slightly behind the movement of the horse and can 'drive' him forwards as necessary. Trainer **A** is in no position to drive the horse and could do little if he decided to stop or turn inwards.

126 Two *ten-minute* sessions are of greater value than *one twenty-minute* session when schooling a young horse.

127 True.

128 False. It is called long-reining and it is used to teach the horse discipline.

129 1 the voice; **2** the lungeing rein; **3** the whip.

130c) Side reins.

Riding technique

131 Yes.

132a) It is called 'playing with the rein' and serves to make the horse alert before moving off.

133 Impulsion.

134b) Outside diagonal.

135 True.

136 The rider has adopted the safest position on a horse which has reared. She has leaned forward and managed to get her arms around the horse's neck which will keep her on the horse. At the same time, she has not pulled on the reins, an action which could unbalance the horse, causing him to topple over backwards.

137b) is correct. Only an expert should attempt to jump off a rearing horse and, even then, such a rider would immediately remount and discipline the horse. If you jump off the horse once he has landed he will think he has achieved his aim and will rear all the more next time. You will also have less control of the horse when on the ground.

138 To ask a horse to turn right, you would first place your *right* leg on the *girth* and your *left* leg behind the *girth*. Then you would apply a little *pressure* on the *right* rein by pulling it back about *half an inch* or so, so that the horse feels the *bit* moving in his mouth.

139 All three sentences are true.

140b) No, she is in danger of falling off if the horse stumbles, which he is more likely to do as her weight is too far forward and is unbalancing him.

Gaits

141 Stride.

142 True.

143a) The muscles of the hindquarters.

144b) Canter.

145 Because the horse needs to raise or lower his head in order to change focus and thus optimise vision.

146 A variation within a gait is when the horse collects or extends (changes the length of his outline and stride).

147a) 6 kmph (4 mph).

148 **A** extended trot; **B** collected trot; **C** working trot; **D** medium trot.

149 Trot.

150b) His head and neck.

Transitions

151a) That the horse goes through the gaits in order to get to the required gait (from walk, through trot to canter, for instance).

152 The horse is moving upwards from walk into trot.

153 An upward transition is one between forward-moving gaits: from walk to trot, and trot to canter, for example. A downwards transition is one between slowing gaits: from canter to trot, or from trot to walk, for example.

154c) Stay in balance.

155 **1** suppleness;   **2** responsiveness;   **3** rider's skill.

Fitness work

156 Inhaling.

157a) Because this is the point when any abnormal respiratory noises may be heard.

158a) Because it makes the horse work harder and saves the strain on the front legs.

159 Conditioning consists of a few weeks' walking on the roads, building up to trotting as and when the horse is coping well.

160 Yes.

161
1 She has shortened her stirrups, which closes the angles between hip, knee and ankle and thus gives her more stability in the saddle.
2 She is looking straight ahead and has inclined her upper body forward, so that at this faster pace she is staying over the horse's centre of gravity.
3 She has shortened the reins to keep control, but is not interfering with the horse's mouth at all.

162 True.

163a) Knee pads.

164 **A** brushing;   **B** speedy cutting;   **C** forging.

165 Interval training.

The country code

166a) Yes. As the farmer owns the land, anyone should get permission before going on it.

167 A RUPP is a Road Used as a Public Path, which means that horses can go on it too. They are often little used and are quite useful as they often link one lane to another, avoiding the busier roads.

168c) is correct. You should not dismount on a ride unless absolutely necessary as you have more control while in the saddle. If the rider had the horse's head over the gate he could barge through it once the catch was freed, and so might catch the rider's legs on the posts.

169 You should not ride on any bridleways as they will quickly become boggy. When they dry out, they will be left in hard ridges which ruins the riding for the whole of the local equestrian population.

170
1 That you always shut gates behind you.
2 That you do not trot or canter past his livestock and so scare it.

Group riding

171a) Split into smaller groups of no more than six horses riding in pairs.

172c) Turn out of the line and rejoin the rear of the ride.

173 Left hand to left hand when passing each other.

174 Wheel.

175 They would have to adjust their speed according to the position they were in. The riders on the inside would have to go slower than those riding towards the outside who may need to extend their horses in order to keep in 'line abreast'.

176a) is about right. Half a length would enable the horse in front to kick the horse behind. Three horses' lengths would prevent the instructor from seeing all horses at once and from keeping the ride working together.

177c) is the only safe course of action. If you allowed any horse to canter off in front of you, the less able rider's horse might decide to follow, ignoring any attempts from his novice rider to stop him!

178 The horse's natural *desire* to be with other horses can work to our *advantage* in some circumstances, especially when we require one horse to *follow* and *copy* another's *actions*.

179 Both the rider at the front and the one at the rear of the ride should give signals at the same time.

180
a) is incorrect as it would only unnerve the young horse;
b) is correct and is the safest method of introducing the young horse to traffic;
c) is incorrect, as the young horse is then directly in the line of the traffic and may panic if he feels the older horse is leaving him behind;
d) is incorrect and would put both horses and riders at risk. The rider on the young horse should be sufficiently competent to cope with the youngster's reactions.

Emergency action

181
A is for: *approach and airway.* (Check that you can approach safely and that the injured party's airway is clear of obstructions.)
B is for: *breathing.* (Check that the injured party is breathing. If not, begin mouth-to-mouth resuscitation.)
C is for: *circulation and cardiac compression.* (Check to see if the rider is bleeding and, if so, stop it by placing a pad over the wound and applying pressure. If the injured party has had a cardiac arrest, you may need to give external cardiac compression – you should learn how to do so before you ever try it for real.)

182a) is correct. You should always assume the worst, in which case the patient should not be moved (unless they are not breathing, in which case the airway should be unblocked) as this could cause fatal damage.

183 Because this avoids the risk of them choking on inhaled blood or vomit.

184 **A** is correct. Rider **B** risks further injury to herself and could damage her horse's mouth.

185 False. You should secure your own horse first, and then assess the casualty and call for help.

186 No.
187 You should never admit liability as this might prejudice your situation

with your insurance company. You should simply exchange insurance details with the other party and leave your insurance company to sort it out.

188
a) Yes, the most accurate and reliable source is the pulse in the carotid artery which is found in the neck.
b) No, in no circumstances should an unconscious person's hat be removed. He or she may have head or neck injuries which may prove fatal if interfered with, so always leave it to the emergency services.

189 You should call the emergency services on 999 as the police will be able to arrange for a local vet to attend immediately. In the meantime, you can pacify your horse. Don't waste time trying to arrange the vet yourself.

190 Shock.

Jumping

191 True.

192 This is an example of poor jumping style. The rider has been totally left behind the horse's movement, which means she had not prepared well enough for the jump and did not go with the horse on take off. She is also looking down, so if the horse was to stumble on landing, she would be very insecure. However, she has managed to slip the reins in order to avoid jabbing the horse in the mouth.

193b) Because it discourages the horse from rushing.

194 A grid.

195a) It enables the horse to be rebalanced before jumping the obstacle.

196 A approach; **B** take-off; **C** flight; **D** landing; **E** getaway.

197 See a stride.

198a) Where the horse does not take a stride inbetween two fences.

199 True.

200
A walk 91 cm–1 m (3–3½ ft)
B trot 1.2–1.4 m (4–4½ ft)